Welcome to your JPA Skills for Dementia Care Learning Resource

Introduction

Welcome to module 310 of the JPA Skills for Dementia Care Learning Resource. This resource will enable you to cascade your knowledge and skills to introduce the concepts of equality, diversity and inclusion that are fundamental to person-centred care practice.

Learning outcomes

On completion of module 310, you will have guided learners to meet the learning outcomes of the Qualifications and Credit Framework Dementia Unit 310.

Learners will:

1. Understand the concept of diversity and its relevance to working with individuals who have dementia.

2. Understand that each individual's experience of dementia is unique.

3. Understand the importance of working in a person-centred way and how this links to inclusion.

Preparation notes

- To deliver this learning resource, you must be knowledgeable and experienced in supporting individuals with dementia. It is recommended that you add to your knowledge by using the Social Care Institute for Excellence (SCIE) free information and e-learning by visiting th⌐ Dementia Gateway at www.scie.org.uk/dementia

- You must read through the entire trainer's guide, familiarising yourself thoroughly with its contents.

- **The Skills for Dementia Care learner's workbook** contains fact sheets and exercises, asking learners to make links, write descriptions discuss issues with you, so do check whether learners have literacy/numeracy difficulties. You may need to speak to their man⍺ supervisor to decide on any required steps to provide your learners with information in a different way.

- The learner's workbook also includes a **learning record**, to show outcomes and the time spent in guided and self-directed learninɡ workbook meets the learning outcomes and assessment criteria of the Qualifications and Credit Framework Dementia Unit 310. is space for you to sign that learners have completed this module and for learners' QCF assessor to sign that the learners have ac the required knowledge level.

- **The Skills for Dementia Care CD** contains the PowerPoint presentation which you will use during your training session. Before the start of the course, you should practise projecting the presentation, to ensure your familiarity with it.

- You will need to print the **confirmation letter** (on your CD) to give to each learner's manager/supervisor. This letter confirms that learners are undertaking module 310 training and indicates the amount of time required to complete the training sessions and work-based activities. It alerts the manager/supervisor to the need to provide ongoing support to each learner and to sign off each learner's learning diary, where indicated.

- You will also need to print the **joining instructions letter** (on your CD). This letter outlines information about the module. You should complete the relevant joining instructions and then send one to each learner, before the first attendance.

- Finally, you should print **certificates** and **evaluations sheets** (on your CD) to give to learners at the end of session 3.

To facilitate the training sessions, you will need:
- flip chart and pens.
- projector and/or laptop.
- PowerPoint presentation (on your CD).
- spare pens and paper for learners, if required.
- Post-It notes.
- a learner's workbook for each learner.
- a certificate and evaluation sheet for each learner.

- You will find a notes box in this trainer's guide, at the end of each session. This is for your own personal use, to record ideas as you develop your skills in using this learning resource.

Confidentiality

Remind learners about the need, during training, to maintain the confidentiality of individuals, carers and others. State clearly that names should not be used and that all information shared during training must not be shared outside of sessions. Learners will need to show their workbook to their manager/supervisor. When asked to provide examples of service users, remind learners to refer to them as 'individual A' or 'Mr/Mrs/Miss A', rather than using any actual names.

Be mindful of any safeguarding issues which may emerge, following your agreed ways of working in addressing these.

Dementia can be a sensitive topic which may arouse deep feelings in carers, so a supportive atmosphere and respect for confidentiality are important. Where issues of concern (personal or work-related) arise during sessions, ensure that individuals are supported to take this up outside of sessions and that an agreement is reached about how to take any issue forward.

Timing

This module has a ten-hour programme of guided learning. This is presented in three sessions. You can choose whether to present the whole programme in one day or to split the programme into half days – or even shorter sessions on separate days.

This module has a further five hours of self-directed learning. There are two self-directed learning activities, of approximately two hours each, to be completed after attending session 2 and before attending session 3. You should agree with learners and their manager/supervisor when this will be completed. Explain that they should record the time taken for these activities in their learning record on pages 39-41 in their workbook. Learners should also undertake a minimum of a one hours' private study, research and reflection. Learners should enter, in their learning record, the time spent and those activities carried out.

Hours of learning: On completion of module 310, learners will be able to provide evidence of the time taken to complete this course of study which meets the hours of learning criteria of the Qualifications and Credit Framework Dementia Unit 310.

To achieve 3 QCF credits, learners will have completed:

- Ten hours' guided learning.
- Five hours' private study.
- Ten hours' assessment with their QCF assessor.

Terminology

The content of this learning resource is written to be accessible and user-friendly. It is in keeping with the drive for personalised services and partnership approaches. The following terms are used:

individual	the person who is being supported/treated/cared for
work setting	the place where the individual is receiving support/treatment/care
agreed ways of working	policies/procedures/contracts/agreements
carer	partner/family/friends/neighbours
others	other professionals supporting/treating/caring for the individual

Assessment Criteria

On completion of module 310, learners will be able to provide evidence of knowledge which meets the assessment criteria of the Qualifications and Credit Framework Dementia Unit 310.

Learners will be able to:

1.1 Explain what is meant by the terms
- Diversity.
- Anti-discriminatory practice.
- Anti-oppressive practice.

1.2 Explain why it is important to recognise and respect an individual's heritage.

1.3 Describe why an individual with dementia may be subjected to discrimination and oppression.

1.4 Describe how discrimination and oppressive practice can be challenged.

2.1 Explain why it is important to identify an individual's specific and unique needs.

2.2 Compare the experience of dementia for an individual who has acquired it as an older person with the experience of an individual who has acquired it as a younger person.

2.3 Describe how the experience of an individual's dementia may impact on carers.

2.4 Describe how the experience of dementia may be different for individuals
- who have a learning disability.
- who are from different ethnic backgrounds.
- at the end of life.

3.1 Explain how current legislation and Government policy supports person-centred working.

3.2 Explain how person-centred working can ensure that an individual's specific and unique needs are met.

3.3 Describe ways of helping an individual's carers or others understand the principles of person-centred care.

3.4 Identify practical ways of helping the individual with dementia maintain their identity.

Content   Page

Session 1. The concept of diversity and its relevance to working with individuals who have dementia

Programme

30 minutes   Welcome and introduction to module 310

45 minutes   **Session 1.1:** What is meant by the terms diversity, anti-discriminatory practice and anti-oppressive practice

45 minutes   **Session 1.2:** The importance of recognising and respecting an individual's heritage

15 minutes   **Break**

45 minutes   **Session 1.3:** Why an individual with dementia may be subjected to discrimination and oppression

45 minutes   **Session 1.4:** How discrimination and oppressive practice can be challenged

NOTE: The timings of this programme are intended as a guide only. You should adapt timings according to discussions at the time and the level of prior knowledge among your group.

Welcome and Introduction

Aim: To welcome and introduce learners to one another and to the learner's workbook.

Time: Allow 30 minutes.

Resources

Flip chart and pens

Projector and/or laptop

PowerPoint slide 1: Skills for Dementia Care – Module 310: Understanding the diversity of individuals with dementia and the importance of inclusion.

PowerPoint slides 2/3: Session 1 – The concept of diversity and its relevance to working with individuals who have dementia and learning objectives

Learner's workbook pages 39-41

- **Show slide 1.** Welcome learners and introduce yourself.

- Provide information about domestic arrangements (fire exits, toilets, smokers' facilities).

- Give learners a learner's workbook or check that they have received one each, if these have been sent to them beforehand.

- Allow five minutes for learners to look through the workbook. Explain that information sheets are included, as well as activities for them to complete and space to write. Clarify that the emphasis is on shared practical learning, rather than formal teaching, based on the knowledge that we can all learn from one another. The success of the learning will depend, therefore, on everyone not only listening, but contributing as fully as possible to discussions.

- Refer learners to the learning record on pages 39-41 in their workbook. Explain that this is a record of learning outcomes and time spent in both guided and self-directed learning. These meet the learning outcomes and the assessment criteria of the Qualifications and Credit Framework Dementia Unit 310.

- Confirm that you will sign the learning record, when learners have completed this module. Explain that there is also space for their QCF assessor to sign that they have achieved the required knowledge level.

- Suggest that learners will need to keep the completed workbook for possible external inspection and for any future employment in the care sector.

- Explain that you have informed each of their managers/supervisors, by letter, that they are undertaking the learning programme.

- Acknowledge that dementia can be a sensitive topic which can arouse deep feelings in carers, so a supportive atmosphere and a respect for confidentiality are important.

- Explain that, where issues of concern (personal or work-related) arise during sessions, they will be taken up outside the sessions, with an agreement reached about how to take any issue forward.

- **Show slides 2/3**: Session 1 – The concept of diversity and its relevance to working with individuals who have dementia. Briefly outline the session's objectives.

Session 1.1: What is meant by the terms diversity, anti-discriminatory practice and anti-oppressive practice

Aim: To enable learners to explain what is meant by the terms

- Diversity
- Anti-discriminatory practice
- Anti-oppressive practice

Time: Allow 45 minutes.

Resources

Flip chart and pens

PowerPoint slide 4: What is meant by these terms?

Learner's workbook pages 6/7

- **Show slide 4** which will reveal three boxes labelled diversity, anti-discriminatory practice and anti-oppressive practice.

- Refer learners to **activity 1** on pages 6/7 in their workbook and read through each of the definitions provided.

- Encourage learners to contribute practical examples that they may have experienced. Add learners' ideas to flip chart sheets each labelled with the three terms.

- Continue to use slide 4 by clicking the mouse to fill the screen with examples of diversity, anti-discriminatory practice and anti-oppressive practice.

- Lead learners through the examples and ask them to call out which box on the slide each example relates to. The correct responses are in the table on page 12 of this Guide.

Terms	Examples
Diversity	Sexuality Social background Gender Age Ethnicity Education
Anti-discriminatory practice	Treating everyone equally Supporting individuals to practice their beliefs Supporting everyone's dignity
Anti-oppressive practice	Facilitating independence Supporting the wishes of the individual Involving individuals in planning their own care

- Suggest that learners use the notes boxes on pages 6/7 in their workbook to list these practical examples next to each term and its definition. Encourage them to offer their own examples and to add these also to their notes.

- Reinforce the **KEY LEARNING POINT**:
  - In order to offer person-centred care, it is important to understand what is meant by diversity, anti-discriminatory practice and anti-oppressive practice.

NOTES

This is for your personal use, to record your ideas as you develop your skills in using this learning resource.

Session 1.2: The importance of recognising and respecting an individual's heritage

Aim: To enable learners to explain why it is important to recognise and respect an individual's heritage.

Time: Allow 45 minutes.

Resources

Flip chart and pens
PowerPoint slide 5: The person-centred theory of dementia
Learner's workbook pages 8/9

- **Show slide 5**. If learners have already explored this theory, briefly remind them of the factors. It this theory is new to learners, explain that understanding each of the factors and how they impact on an individual, is a helpful way of understanding the individual's experience of dementia.

- Refer learners to the Biography factor and explain how an understanding of an individual's heritage supports specific and unique needs to be met. Ask learners to call out examples of biographical information. Ideas should include: where they grew up, what they did (work/ raising a family), religion and spirituality.

- Ask the learners to work in pairs and discuss each other's backgrounds, considering cultural influences and events that were important in their lives. Remind the learners they need only share information that they feel comfortable with sharing. Ask each pair to introduce each other to the group and share some of what they have learned about each other's heritage.

- After the learners have completed their discussion, ask them to complete **activity 2** on page 8 in their workbook. Allow 10 minutes.

- Ask learners to share their feelings with the rest of the group and reinforce that these same feelings will be experienced by individuals with dementia.

- Refer learners to **activity 3** on page 9 in their workbook and suggest they record the positive feelings that can be experienced. Allow 5 minutes.

- Ask learners to share their ideas with the rest of the group. These should include a sense of pride, belonging, self-respect etc.

- Discuss ways of minimising feelings of discomfort for individuals with dementia when supporting them to share information about themselves. Suggest that learners make a note of these ways in the relevant notes box on page 9 in their workbook. Some ideas for you to lead this discussion include: sharing information in a private location, being in a place with minimal distractions, using old photographs or objects to help the individual recall information more accurately and, sharing information with carers or others who know the individual well.

- Reinforce with learners that the basic principle is that information sharing must be on a 'need to know' basis. Care staff and others must follow their organisations policy and procedure to ensure that information is shared legally, ethically and safely. They must follow the organisation's policy on confidentiality and information sharing. Discuss when it is permissible to share information about an individual with others:

  - When the individual with dementia has agreed that it can be shared. If an individual has explicitly stated that they do not want information about them shared with another person, this must be respected

  - If they have not agreed but there is an overriding legal reason to disclose – related to risk of harm to self or others, or a safeguarding investigation.

  - If an individual does not have the capacity to consent to information being shared (sometimes even if they do have capacity), it can only be done if it can be shown with evidence that it is in the individuals best interests to have the information shared.

- Reinforce the **KEY LEARNING POINTS:**
  - Sharing information in an appropriate way, about an individual's heritage can promote a sense of well-being and improve communication.
  - Having an understanding of an individual's heritage can help others meet the individual's unique needs.
  - Information should always be shared in a sensitive manner.

NOTES

This is for your personal use, to record your ideas as you develop your skills in using this learning resource.

Session 1.3: Why an individual with dementia may be subjected to discrimination and oppression

Aim: To enable learners to describe why an individual with dementia may be subjected to discrimination and oppression.

Time: Allow 45 minutes.

Resources
Flip chart and pens
Post-it notes
Learner's workbook page 10

- Ask learners to get into small groups of approximately 4 people (dependent on the size of the group). Ask them to consider what they have learned from so far in this module and to discuss what the barriers are to anti-discriminatory and anti-oppressive practice.

- Ask each small group to record their ideas on post-it notes. Reinforce that this exercise is about identifying the barriers. Learners will look at solutions in the next session. Allow 20 minutes for this exercise.

- While the small groups are working on this prepare a flip chart sheet by marking it with a central line to form two columns headed **Discrimination** and **Oppression**.

- Ask each small group to elect a spokesperson to feed back the ideas of their group.

- Discuss with the whole group whether these ideas are a result of discrimination or oppression. Ask the spokesperson to stick their post-it notes on the relevant column on the flip chart sheet. Some examples to support your discussion are in the table on page 18 of this Guide.

- Stress to the learners that there are no particular right answers as many of their ideas will be based on opinion and that some barriers may fit across both practices. The most important issue to consider is how many of the barriers can create discrimination and oppression for the individual with dementia.

Possible solutions to activity 4.

Why an individual may be subjected to discrimination and oppression	
Discrimination	Oppression
Beliefs	Personality type
Values	Institutionalised routines and regimes
Stereotyping	Lack of time
Previous experiences	Lack of money for resources
Lack of training and education	Guilt
	Fear

- Allow time for the group to copy the ideas from the post-it notes onto the relevant boxes in **activity 4** on page 10 in their workbook.

- Reinforce the **KEY LEARNING POINT**:
  - Individuals with dementia may be subjected to discrimination and oppression as a result of the attitudes of others and situations that are barriers to good care.

NOTES

This is for your personal use, to record your ideas as you develop your skills in using this learning resource.

Session 1.4: How discrimination and oppressive practice can be challenged

Aim: To enable learners to describe how discrimination and oppressive practice can be challenged.

Time: Allow 45 minutes.

Resources

Flip chart and pens
A5 paper
Learner's workbook pages 11-13

- Ask learners to stay in the same groups as for the last activity and refer them to **activity 5** on page 11 in their workbook.

- Ask learners to read through the questionnaire and to discuss in their group, what each action may look like towards an individual with dementia. Explain that they should record their ideas in the table on page 12 in their workbook and that they will then discuss these ideas with the entire group of learners. Allow 20 minutes.

- Ask the small groups to share their ideas and lead a discussion with learners to explore the role they might play in challenging discrimination and oppressive practice towards individuals with dementia. Suggest to learners that they use the notes box on page 13 in their workbook to record these possible solutions.

- The table on page 21 of this Guide gives some examples of the discriminatory and oppressive practices that individuals with dementia might experience.

- Reinforce the **KEY LEARNING POINT:**
  - Discriminatory and oppressive practice can be challenged and there are many ways of achieving this.

Action	Examples relating to individuals with dementia
Stereotyping jokes	Jokes about the individual's memory difficulties or behaviour.
Discriminatory remarks	Negative comments and disparaging remarks about the difficulties an individual has because of his or her dementia (eg. "he has lost his marbles", "she's not all there").
Not creating opportunities	Seeing only the difficulties an individual has and not recognising their abilities. Having disabling environments.
Not having conversations about equality	Not talking to individuals about their rights. Not including carers and others in care planning to support equal opportunities for individuals.
Organisational discrimination	Naming care settings by the difficulties individuals have (eg. The dementia unit; the challenging behaviour wing). Routines and procedures that restrict or oppress individuals. (eg. set "toileting time", not allowing an individual to make their own decisions even when they can).
Discriminatory and oppressive vocabulary	Task-based language (eg. "Toileting them", "Feeding them"). Accusations and blame (eg. "You have made a mess"). Controlling (eg. "You are not allowed").
Ineffective complaints procedures	Complaints procedures not easy to follow. Confidentiality is not respected. No follow-up to complaints or follow-up is not transparent.
Not speaking for others	No advocacy for individuals with communication difficulties. No reporting or recording of issues.
Not valuing diversity	Not recognising the unique experience of dementia for every individual. Seeing all individuals with dementia as the same.
Not challenging discrimination	Not being person-centred in attitudes or actions. Not speaking out for the rights of individuals who cannot speak for themselves.

NOTES

This is for your personal use, to record your ideas as you develop your skills in using this learning resource.

Session 2. Understanding that each individual's experience of dementia is unique

Programme

15 minutes **Summary of Session 1.**

40 minutes **Session 2.1:** Why it is important to identify an individual's specific and unique needs

40 minutes **Session 2.2:** The experience of dementia for individuals of different ages

15 minutes **Break**

40 minutes **Session 2.3:** How the experience of an individual's dementia may impact on carers

45 minutes **Session 2.4:** The diverse experience of dementia

NOTE: The timings of this programme are intended as a guide only. You should adapt timings according to discussions at the time and the level of prior knowledge among your group.

Summary of Session 1.

Aim: To enable learners to reflect on what has been learned from the previous session.

Time: Allow 15 minutes.

Resources

flip chart and pens
projector and/or laptop
PowerPoint slides 6/7: Session 2 - Understanding that each individual's experience of dementia is unique and learning objectives
PowerPoint slide 8: Summary of learning from Session 1

- If you are leading this session on a separate date from session 1, refer to pages 9/10 of this guide to welcome learners back.

- **Show slides 6/7** and briefly outline the session's objectives.

- **Show slide 8** and summarise the key points that were covered during session 1

- Ask learners to reflect on what they have learned during session 1 and use the flip chart to note key points learnt and areas for further development. Tell learners that you will be reflecting back on this list at the end of session 3.

Session 2.1: Why it is important to identify an individual's specific and unique needs

Aim: To enable learners to explain why it is important to identify an individual's specific and unique needs.

Time: Allow 40 minutes.

Resources

Flip chart and pens
Learner's workbook pages 15/16

- Refer learners to **activity 6** on page 15 in their workbook and read the first paragraph with them.

- Ask learners to consider how they feel at this moment in time. Are they hot, cold, excited, uncomfortable, thirsty, interested, sleepy?

- Ask learners to discuss with the person next to them what they need to address these feelings. Ask them to use the left column of the table in activity 6 to make notes (What I need at this moment in time). Allow 10 minutes.

- Ask learners to share the needs they have listed with the group. Encourage them to discuss if there are similarities or differences in their needs. Identify if there are some predominant needs amongst the group.

- Refer learners to the right column of the table in activity 6. Ask them to complete it by listing the behaviours they might display to indicate these needs. Again, ask the learners to compare these potential behaviours amongst the group and lead a discussion about why learners are not displaying these behaviours and what is stopping them.

- Refer learners to **activity 7** on page 16 in their workbook. Explore with learners why an individual with dementia may not control their behaviours in the same way. Reinforce that for some individuals, neurological damage may cause them to be less able to understand and make sense of situations, or to control their behaviours in response. Some possible effects on the behaviours of individuals are in the notes on page 26 of this Guide. Ask learners to make notes in the box provided on page 16 in their workbook.

If an individual has no sense of what will happen in the future, how might this affect their behaviour?

- Lack of concern for the needs of others.
- Lack of insight into own safety.
- Expressions of frustration, impatience or anger.

If an individual is making sense of current situations by drawing on memories of previous experiences, how might this affect their behaviour?

- Acting out old behaviours (work roles, social roles).
- Confabulating (describing events that have not happened, but may have at a previous time in the individual's experience).
- Emotional expressions that appear to be incongruent or inappropriate to the situation.

- Discuss why learners must identify an individual's specific and unique needs. Ideas should include: enhancing a sense of well-being, maintaining skills and, maintaining a sense of self.

- Reinforce the **KEY LEARNING POINTS:**
  - Individuals with dementia may live in the present and not have an understanding of what is going to happen next.
  - Individuals with dementia may be drawing on old memories to make sense of current situations
  - Needs are unique and specific to each individual.
  - Individuals with dementia often express their unique and specific needs through their behaviour.

NOTES

This is for your personal use, to record your ideas as you develop your skills in using this learning resource.

Session 2.2: The experience of dementia for individuals of different ages

Aim: To enable learners to compare the experience of dementia for an individual who has acquired it as an older person with the experience of an individual who has acquired it as a younger person.

Time: Allow 40 minutes.

Resources

flip chart and pens
Learner's workbook pages 17-19

- Discuss with learners, what is a 'younger age' and at what age is an individual considered to be 'older'. Explore with learners which category they consider themselves to be in. Discuss how, even in 'older peoples' services, there can be large age gaps between those in their early 60's to those in their 100's.

- Reinforce that whilst pensionable age is usually used as a defining point between 'younger' and 'older', this is a subjective viewpoint.

- Refer learners to **activity 8** on pages 17/18 in their workbook. Allow time for them to read through both case studies.

- When all learners have read the case studies ask them to form into two groups. Ask one group to consider the similarities and the other group to consider the differences in the experience of dementia for each of the two case studies.

- Ask each group to feedback their list of similarities and differences. Some examples are listed on page 29 of this Guide for your use. Write their ideas on the flip chart, separated into two columns for similarities and differences.

- Lead a discussion about factors that are impacting on the experience of the two women, such as the personalities of all of the individuals involved, the values and beliefs, society and individual attitudes, resources that are available.

- Once the learners have completed this activity ask them if there are any other points they might like to make. These may include some ideas for addressing the likely different needs of individuals with dementia at different ages. Note any other suggestions onto the flipchart. Allow learners time to make notes of the suggestions in the box on page 19 in their workbook.

Similarities in experience	Differences in experience
• Both have dementia with similar signs. • Both women have family support. • Both families have difficulty supporting the women. • Both families are unhappy about the admission.	• Although their dementia presents in a similar way, only Agatha is in an environment that meets her needs. • People expect Agatha to have a condition such as dementia but they do not expect a young person like Alex to have it. • Agatha's family are informed about dementia. • Dan believes he has caused Alex's admission by his behaviour. • Alex's children are dependent on her. • Agatha's children have been supporting her and George for some time.

• Reinforce the **KEY LEARNING POINTS:**

  • There are key similarities and differences between the experience of dementia for an individual who has acquired it as an older person with the experience of an individual who has acquired it as a young person.

  • The provision of person-centred care and support to an individual with dementia takes into account the unique experience of dementia for all individuals.

NOTES

This is for your personal use, to record your ideas as you develop your skills in using this learning resource.

Session 2.3: How the experience of an individual's dementia may impact on carers

Aim: To enable learners to describe how the experience of an individual's dementia may impact on carers

Time: Allow 40 minutes.

Resources
Flip chart and pens
PowerPoint slides 9, 10 and 11
Learner's workbook pages 17/18 and 20-24

- Introduce this session by asking learners to call out the roles and activities they undertake on a daily basis. Write these on the flip chart.

- Refer learners to **activity 9** on page 20 in their workbook. Explain to learners that they are going to continue to use the information from the two case studies on pages 17/18 in their workbook to identify the roles and activities that are likely to have been undertaken by Alex and Agatha prior to their having dementia. Ask them to work in pairs and allow 10 minutes.

- Ask learners to feed back their ideas which may include: Roles of: mother, daughter, wife, housewife, worker. Activities of: caring, supporting family members, domestic activities, leisure activities, financial management, social activities.

- Lead a discussion with learners about:

  • Who might carry out these roles and activities now?

  • Is it likely that some of these roles and activities will have been abandoned?

  • What is the impact likely to be on the individual with dementia

  • What is the impact likely to be on carers?

  Suggest that learners use the notes box on page 20 to record some of these ideas.

- **Show slide 9** and refer learners to **Information sheet 1** on page 21 in their workbook. Read through the first two paragraphs with learners. Suggest they use the notes box to draw the illustration on the slide . Reinforce that this is an illustration of personhood being met for two individuals who are giving equally to an interaction.

- **Show slide 10** and read through the third paragraph on page 21 in learner's workbooks. Suggest that learners use the notes box on page 22 to draw the illustration on the slide . Reinforce that this is an illustration of personhood not being met because the two individuals are not connecting with their communication.

- **Show slide 11** and read through the first paragraph on page 22 in learner's workbooks. Suggest that learners use the notes box on page 22 to draw the illustration on the slide . Reinforce that this is an illustration of personhood being met for two individuals when each is giving all that they can to the interaction.

- Discuss what everyone has learned from this session and use the flip chart to record the key learning points. Suggest that learners record these in the final notes box for this session on page 22 in the workbook. Some points are listed below for your guidance.

  - The experience of dementia impacts on carers as they have to adopt new roles and activities.

  - Many carers start to feel isolated when communication becomes more difficult.

  - Individuals with dementia and their carers can experience well-being and fulfilment when they can connect through their interactions with each other.

- Refer learners to the self-directed learning activity on pages 23/24 in their workbook. Explain that learners will complete this learning activity away from the workshop. It should take approximately two hours. Learners may discuss with their manager/supervisor how they take this time.

- Explain that the self-directed learning activity is an opportunity for learners to further research how the experience of an individual's dementia may impact on carers. They may like to use some of the resources offered on page 23 in their workbook or they may search for others. Suggest that learners who have drawn on their own study and research should record the source in the notes box and share this information with other learners when they return to Session 3.

- Learners should be prepared to discuss their learning from this self-directed learning activity when they attend Session 3. Remind them to record the time taken in this activity in their learning record on page 40 in their workbook.

NOTES

This is for your personal use, to record your ideas as you develop your skills in using this learning resource.

Session 2.4: The diverse experience of dementia

Aim: To enable learners to describe the how the experience of dementia may be different for individuals who have a learning disability, who are from different ethnic backgrounds, or who are at the end of life.

Time: Allow 45 minutes.

Resources

Flip chart and pens
PowerPoint Slide 12: The person-centred theory of dementia
Learner's workbook pages 25/26

- **Show slide 12** and remind learners that this is an illustration of the person-centred theory of dementia. Explain that each of the factors can be used to understand how the experience of dementia might be different for individuals who have a learning disability, who are from different ethnic backgrounds or who are at the end of life.

- Refer learners to **activity 10** on pages 25/26 in their workbook. Ask them to separate into three groups. Allocate each group a case study:
  - Case study 1 – Learning disability
  - Case study 2 – Different ethnic backgrounds
  - Case study 3 – End of life

- Ask the groups to consider their allocated case study using the person-centred factors and to record their reflections on a sheet of flip chart paper. Allow 20 minutes.

- Ask each group to nominate a spokesperson to feedback the group reflections to the rest of the group.

- Discuss where the key differences lie between each of the different cases and how the experience of dementia may be different for each of them. Ideas to help you and the group are in the table on page 35 of your Guide

- Allow the learners' time to record their reflections in the notes box on page 26 in their workbooks.

Ideas to help the groups may include:

Person-centred Factors	Individuals with a learning disability and dementia	Individuals from different ethnic backgrounds	Individuals at the end of their life
Personality	May be expressed differently because of the influences of those around them.	The expression of their qualities and traits will be partially influenced by their ethnic background, culture and beliefs.	The expression of their qualities and traits might be influenced by factors such as pain, discomfort, distress or, spiritual beliefs.
Biography	May be influenced by frustration or anger because of reduced abilities and a lack of understanding from others.	May be influenced by cultural expectations and rituals.	May be influenced by pain and the environment that the individual is in eg. hospital.
Health	May develop dementia at an earlier age than those without a learning disability.	Food choices may be important for individuals from different ethnic backgrounds. An individual may forget that a food choice is important.	Life functions start to shut down. Mental health may be affected.
Neurological State	Have a higher risk of having Alzheimer's disease. May be more difficult to assess because many assessments of neurological state are measures of ability against a baseline of individuals who previously were cognitively able.	There may be cultural beliefs and practices that, if professionals do not understand, result in errors of diagnosis and inappropriate care and support. For example, a delusion is a false belief not amenable to reason and out of context with a person's cultural and religious beliefs: diagnosing someone as deluded must take into account cultural and religious factors.	May become more confused as body systems slow down or because of the impact of pain relieving medication.
Social Psychology	May be used to communal living. May be less supported by others who also have learning disabilities in their community. May have moved to live in a care setting for older individuals who have little in common with the individual with a learning disability	May have extended family networks. May have difficulty communicating if English is a second language. May have different social rules for communicating with others (eg. use of touch or eye contact).	May have to rely on social contacts visiting them. May be less inclined to interact with others as the individual becomes more withdrawn.

- Reinforce the **KEY LEARNING POINT:**

  - The experience of dementia may be different for individuals who have a learning disability, who are from different ethnic backgrounds, or who are at the end of life.

- Refer learners to the self-directed learning activity on page 27 in their workbook. Explain that learners will complete this learning activity away from the workshop. It should take approximately two hours. Learners may discuss with their manager/supervisor how they take this time.

- Explain that the self-directed learning activity is an opportunity for learners to further research how the experience of dementia may be different for individuals who have a learning disability, who are from different ethnic backgrounds, or who are at the end of life. They may like to use the resource offered on page 27 in their workbook or they may search for others. Suggest that learners record the source of their information in the notes box and share this information with other learners, when they return to Session 3.

- Learners should be prepared to discuss their learning from this self-directed learning activity, when they attend Session 3. Remind them to record the time taken in this activity in their learning record on page 40 in their workbook.

- Confirm the date, venue and start and finish time for Session 3.

NOTES

This is for your personal use, to record your ideas as you develop your skills in using this learning resource.

Session 3. Understanding the importance of working in a person-centred way and how this links to inclusion

Programme

15 minutes	**Welcome, introduction and summary of Session 2**
40 minutes	**Session 3.1:** Current legislation and Government policy supporting person-centred working
40 minutes	**Session 3.2:** How person-centred working can ensure that an individual's specific and unique needs are met
15 minutes	**Break**
40 minutes	**Session 3.3:** Ways of helping an individual's carers or others understand the principles of person-centred care
45 minutes	**Session 3.4:** Practical ways of helping the individual with dementia maintain their identity
30 minutes	**End of Module 310:** Recording learning

NOTE: The timings of this programme are intended as a guide only. You should adapt timings according to discussions at the time and the level of prior knowledge among your group.

Welcome, introduction and summary of Session 2

Aims: To welcome learners back and to introduce them to session 3. To allow learners to reflect on what has been learned from the previous sessions.

Time: Allow 15 minutes.

Resources

Flipchart and pens

Projector and/or laptop

PowerPoint slide 13: Skills for Dementia Care – Module 310: Understanding the diversity of individuals with dementia and the importance of inclusion

PowerPoint slides 14/15: Session 3 – Understanding the importance of working in a person-centred way and how this links to inclusion and learning objectives

PowerPoint slide 16: Summary of learning from Session 2

- **Show slide 13**. Welcome learners and introduce this half-day session as the final guided learning element of this module. Provide information about domestic arrangements (fire exits, toilets, smokers' facilities).

- Check that everyone has brought the learner's workbook along.

- Remind learners that dementia can be a sensitive topic which can arouse deep feelings in carers, so a supportive atmosphere and a respect for confidentiality are important.

- Explain that, where issues of concern (personal or work-related) arise during sessions, they will be taken up outside of sessions, with an agreement reached about how to take any issue forward.

- **Show slides 14/15**: Session 3 – Understanding the importance of working in a person-centred way and how this links to inclusion. Briefly outline the session's objectives.

- **Show slide 16** and summarise the key points that were covered during Session 2

- Ask learners to reflect on what they have learned during Session 2 and use the flip chart to note key points learnt and areas for further development. Tell the learners that you will be reflecting back on this list at the end of session 3.

NOTES

This is for your personal use, to record your ideas as you develop your skills in using this learning resource.

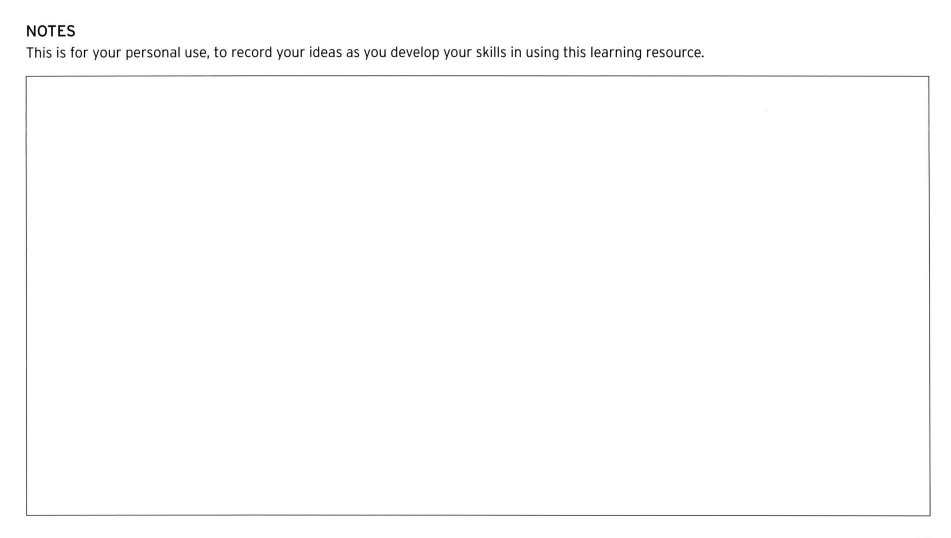

Session 3.1: Current legislation and Government policy supporting person-centred working

Aim: To enable learners to explain how current legislation and Government policy supports person-centred working.

Time: Allow 40 minutes.

Resources

Flip chart and pens
Projector and/or laptop
PowerPoint slide 17: Current legislation and government policy
Learner's workbook pages 29-32

- **Show slide 17** and refer learners to **Information sheet 2** on pages 29-32 in their workbook. Discuss with the group how these policies fit with person-centred care.

- Ask the group to work in pairs to identify the aspects of each piece of legislation and Government policy that supports person-centred working. Suggest that they underline the relevant words or sentences in the information sheet. Allow 20 minutes.

- Ask the group to feed back their ideas about how some legislation and Government policy can support person-centred working and note these on the flip chart. Lead a discussion about how and why even with this, person-centred ways of working may not happen. Suggest that learners make a note of the discussion points in the notes box on page 32 in their workbook.

- Explain to learners that they should use this information as a reference point. Suggest that they gather further information regarding this legislation and these policies during private study and in discussions with their manager or supervisor.

- Reinforce the **KEY LEARNING POINT:**

  - Current legislation and government policy can be used to support person-centred practice, but it needs good leadership and management to ensure this happens.

NOTES

This is for your personal use, to record your ideas as you develop your skills in using this learning resource.

Session 3.2: How person-centred working can ensure that an individual's specific and unique needs are met

Aim: To enable learners to explain how person-centred working can ensure that an individual's specific and unique needs are met.

Time: Allow 40 minutes.

Resources

Flip chart and pens
PowerPoint slide 18
Learner's workbook pages 27 and 33/34

- Refer learners to **activity 11** on page 33 in their workbook. Ask the learners to work in pairs to complete this activity. Explain that this exercise reinforces the importance of understanding the specific and unique needs of an individual by fully understanding their life history. Allow 10 minutes

- Ask learners to feed back their ideas. Use the notes in this table to guide your discussion

Person-centred Factor	Specific and unique needs
Personality	Needs privacy and to spend time alone. Needs to express his loyalty to others.
Biography	Needs understanding of his fears - with care taken to not create a situation that fits with his past experiences.
Health	None known.
Neurological State	Needs supporting to live well at the care home, he believes he is still living an Army life, possibly in the war prison. Needs understanding from others that his neurological damage may cause him to not use logic and reasoning in response to his fears.
Social Psychology	Needs relationship building with only one or two people to give him a sense of security whilst respecting his need for solitude.

- Lead a discussion using the following questions:

  - What needs were similar?
  - Were there possibilities for errors in interpretation of his behaviour?
  - How might needs be identified when working with individuals in the work place?
  - Which elements of the person-centred approach particularly helped you to identify needs?

- Suggest to learners that they make notes on these discussions in the appropriate box on page 34 in their workbook.

- Refer learner's to page 27 in their workbook when they completed the self-directed learning activity to research how the experience of dementia may be different for individuals who have a learning disability, who are from different ethnic backgrounds, or who are at the end of life.

- Encourage learners to discuss their learning from this self-directed learning activity and to apply this to understanding how person-centred working ensures that the diverse needs of individuals are met. Reinforce the importance of person-centred relationships in meeting these needs.

- **Show slide 18** and explain to the learners that a person-centred relationship is achieved when a care worker is in a state of:

  Congruence – when there is a correspondence of values and beliefs between the carers and the individual with dementia.
  Acceptance – when the carer or others do not judge an individual by their looks or actions.
  Empathy – when the carer or others can sense and understand the individual's feelings.

- Suggest that learners label the diagram on page 34 in their workbook, using these descriptions to guide them.

- Reinforce the **KEY LEARNING POINT** that:

  - Person-centred working ensures that specific and unique needs are met.

NOTES

This is for your personal use, to record your ideas as you develop your skills in using this learning resource.

Session 3.3: Ways of helping an individual's carers or others understand the principles of person-centred care

Aim: To enable learners to describe ways of helping an individual's carers or others understand the principles of person-centred care.

Time: Allow 40 minutes.

Resources

Flip chart and pens
Learner's workbook pages 27 and 35/36

- Explain to learners that you are going to tell them a story. Ask them to close their eyes (if they feel comfortable) and try to imagine what is happening:

"You are sat on a comfortable seat in the first class carriage of a train travelling with your partner across Asia. Your partner has treated you to this trip as a surprise and you have been on the train for three days, stopping every evening to experience a wonderful meal at an excellent restaurant. You have just had lunch and you are dosing in your seat. The sounds of the train are lulling you to sleep."

- Ask the learners ......'HOW DO YOU FEEL'............... record learners' responses on the flip chart........continue the story.

"Suddenly, you become aware that the train is coming to an abrupt stop. You sit up and look around. The train has stopped at a station; you were unaware that the train was going to stop..... You thought the next destination would not be reached until the evening. You look to your partner for an explanation but they are not there!"

- Ask the learners......'HOW DO YOU FEEL'..........record learners' responses on the flip chart.......continue the story.

"You stand up and look around the carriage, where are they? You walk down the length of the carriage looking for them but they are not there......"

- Ask the learners ...'WHAT WOULD YOU DO NEXT?'....record the learners' responses on the flip chart...continue the story.

"You search the next carriage and the toilets, you ask the guard but he does not speak English."

- Ask the learners ……'HOW DO YOU FEEL?'…….continue the story.

"You return to your seat, after ten minutes your partner returns with a bottle of Champagne!"

- Ask the learners……'HOW DO YOU FEEL, WHAT WOULD YOU DO OR SAY?'

- Refer learners to the feelings and behaviours recorded on the flip chart. Remind them that these are behaviours often demonstrated by individuals with dementia. Reinforce how by using our own experiences of an event we can see how an individual may behave if they believe that event is really happening to them. By having an understanding of the individual's perceptions, beliefs and feelings, we are more able to address an individual's specific and unique needs.

- Refer learners to **activity 12** on page 35 in their workbook. Suggest that they record the feelings and behaviours that are listed on the flip chart, in the first box.

- Ask learners to discuss in pairs, how the story helped them to understand the need for a person-centred approach. They should record their ideas in the second box and be prepared to share these with the rest of the group. Allow 10 minutes

- Refer learners to page 27 in their workbook and remind them of the self-directed activity that they completed. Lead a discussion with learners about how this message might be given to carers and others to help them to understand the diverse experience of dementia and how the principles of person-centred care can be applied to meet the individual's specific and unique needs.

- Record learners' ideas on the flipchart. Ask the group to identify the most useful strategies. These might include: story telling; attendance on courses with care workers; access to e-learning and books; support groups with other carers; role modelling and demonstration and, involving the carer in assessment and care planning.

- Allow learners time to record these ideas in the third box on page 35 in their workbook.

- **Show slide 19** and refer learners to the key learning points on page 36 in their workbook.

NOTES

This is for your personal use, to record your ideas as you develop your skills in using this learning resource.

Session 3.4: Practical ways of helping the individual with dementia maintain their identity

Aim: To enable learners to identify practical ways of helping the individual with dementia maintain their identity.

Time: Allow 45 minutes.

Resources

Flip chart and pens
PowerPoint slide 20: Practical ideas for maintaining the personal identity of the individual
Learner's workbook page 37

- **Show slide 20** and discuss the examples of how personal identity might be maintained for an individual. Encourage learners to offer their ideas.

- Refer learners to **activity 13** on page 37 in their workbook. Ask learners to work in pairs or small groups and to select one of the case studies from the previous sessions in this module or an individual who they currently work. They should apply the ideas on the slide to produce an example of how the identity of their chosen individual might be maintained. Ask each pair or small group to record their ideas on a sheet of flip chart paper and explain that they will present their ideas back to the group. If the learners use real people as their case study ask them to change the individual's identity in order to retain confidentiality for that individual. Allow 20 minutes.

- Ask each pair or small group of learners to present their ideas to the main group. Encourage discussion and suggest that learners add the ideas of others to their notes. There are some notes provided on page 50 of this Guide to assist you.

- Reinforce the **KEY LEARNING POINTS:**

  - There are many practical ways to maintain an individual's identity.

  - In a person-centred approach there will be different ways of supporting each individual as each will have specific and unique needs.

Person-centred care	Practical ideas include
Dignity How this can be maintained.	Valuing and encouraging the individual's resilience or 'fighting spirit'. Providing opportunities for private conversations. Providing private environments for care needs. Supporting privacy of the body during intimate care.
Respect Acknowledgement of the individual's identity.	Addressing the individual by their preferred name. Valuing the individual's biography, including their cultural, spiritual and ethnic background. Including the individual in conversations and activity. Connecting with the individual through appropriate touch and eye contact.
Choice What the individual would like to do.	Listening to and supporting individuals to express their needs and wants. Offering options in everyday activities. Involving the individual in planning their own care. Respecting the individual's choice.
Independence How to enable an individual.	Recognising the individual's abilities. Breaking down an activity into manageable stages. Only stepping in to help with support for the aspects of an activity that the individual cannot do. Providing environmental features to support the individual.
Rights How can these be maintained to meet the individual's values and beliefs.	Consulting with the individual, carers and others to understand the values and beliefs of the individual. Checking for written records of the individual's previously expressed values and beliefs. Providing the individual with information in a format that is understandable.

NOTES

This is for your personal use, to record your ideas as you develop your skills in using this learning resource.

End of Module 310: recording learning

Time: Allow 30 minutes.

Resources

PowerPoint slide 21 – key learning points from module 310
Learner's workbook pages 39-41
evaluation sheets
certificates

- **Show slide 21** and reinforce the learning from this module.

- Refer back to the flip chart lists that you completed with the group at the start of Sessions 2 and 3. Identify any areas that had been recorded as areas for further development and that have now been achieved. Suggest to learners that they should address any areas where they still need to develop their knowledge and understanding by discussing their learning needs with their manager.

- Support learners in completing the learning record on pages 39-41 in their workbook. They should enter the time taken in total in guided learning. This will be approximately ten hours. Sign the appropriate box in the learning record and return them to the learners.

- Also explain that learners should enter the time taken in self-directed learning. This should be approximately four hours in total for the two self-directed learning activities and a further hour of private study and research. Learners should enter, in their learning record, those activities carried out.

- On completion of this session, give out the evaluation forms and ask learners to complete them and return them to you.

- Give out certificates of attendance for this course. If learners are undertaking a QCF qualification, you will need to arrange for a further certificate from the Awarding Organisation. This further certificate will be awarded when the QCF Assessor has signed the confirmation in the learning record, that assessment has taken place.

- Thank learners for attending module 310 and inform them that there are further modules for dementia care in this JPA Skills for Dementia Care series.